1880

In an effort to help improve science instruction in New York City schools, Albert Bickmore develops the Museum's first formal educational program: a zoology lecture course for teachers that incorporates Museum specimens and lantern slides.

1894

Robert E. Peary discovers the site of the first of three large Cape York meteorite fragments in Greenland. The fragments are deposited at the Museum 10 years later, arriving on a carriage drawn by 28 horses. The largest, a 34-ton (27-metric ton) fragment, is so heavy that it is supported by posts that extend down to the bedrock beneath the Museum.

1896

The Ethnological Hall opens on the first floor. It later becomes the Hall of Northwest Coast Indians.

1899

Trustee J.P. Morgan helps the Museum purchase a collection of 382 American gems that gemologist George F. Kunz had selected for an exhibition by Tiffany & Co. at the 1889 Exposition Universelle in Paris.

1908

Museum dinosaur-hunter Barnum Brown discovers the fossil skeleton of the *Tyrannosaurus rex* on display today.

1909

The first public showing of a motion picture at the Museum takes place on New Year's Day, when ornithologist Frank Chapman uses film in his public lecture about Florida bird life. Six years earlier, Chapman had helped persuade President Theodore Roosevelt to designate the first federal bird reservation on Florida's Pelican Island.

1912

The Museum installs the Mainka 990-lb (450-kg) seismograph—the largest instrument in the U.S. for recording earthquake shocks—on the ground floor.

1936

President Franklin D. Roosevelt dedicates the Theodore Roosevelt Memorial, New York's official memorial to its 33rd governor and the nation's 26th president, at the Museum.

1937

The Hayden Planetarium–Grace Peruvian Eclipse Expedition travels to Peru to observe the total solar eclipse on June 8. An aerial photographer takes the first pictures of an eclipse from the upper atmosphere at 25,000 feet (7,620 meters), while the expedition artist paints four canvases recording the eclipse and two of the southern sky.

1942

Museum ornithologist Ernst Mayr publishes *Systematics and the Origin of Species*, one of several major works to reconcile evidence from the new field of genetics with Charles Darwin's theory of natural selection. Later that decade, paleontologist George Simpson offers evidence from the fossil record. Their work contributes to the modern theory of evolution, known as the modern synthesis.

1943

The Museum contributes to the war effort with expertise about remote areas in the Pacific where scientists have conducted fieldwork, including tips on field gear design and identifying dangerous insects and snakes. The Hayden Planetarium offers demonstrations in celestial navigation.

THE ULTIMATE GUIDE

American Museum of Natural History

The Ultimate Guide

ASHTON APPLEWHITE

STERLING
New York

CONTENTS

INTRODUCTION

Whether this book is a souvenir of your visit to the Museum or the starting point of your exploration into everything we have to offer, we welcome you to the American Museum of Natural History, a place of limitless wonder, discovery, and lifelong inspiration!

The Museum was founded in 1869 by a group of civic-minded individuals who believed strongly that New York City ought to have a center for natural science and a home for "popular instruction" about the natural world and human cultures. For generations, the Museum has been just that, pursuing a mission "to discover, interpret, and disseminate—through scientific research and education—knowledge about human cultures, the natural world, and the universe," while continually pioneering the ways it studies the world and reaches and teaches a broad and diverse audience.

With 45 permanent exhibition halls housed in 25 interconnected buildings including the Rose Center for Earth and Space, the Museum covers 1.6 million square feet on an 18-acre campus on the Upper West Side of Manhattan. Its permanent galleries offer a "field guide" to the natural world and global cultures, while topical special exhibitions present and explain the complex issues of our times. The Museum welcomes some five million people from around the world annually. Many millions more are touched through our traveling exhibitions and Space Shows, by visiting us at amnh.org, and participating in our many other digital and online offerings. Underpinning everything the Museum does and everything you see in the galleries is a vibrant program of scientific research, conducted by a scientific staff of 200—biologists and paleontologists, astrophysicists and anthropologists, among others. At the center of this research enterprise is a world-renowned collection of 32 million specimens and artifacts, an irreplaceable record of life on Earth, now joined by newer forms of collections such as frozen tissue and astrophysics and genomics data. Working at the frontiers of science in such areas as comparative genomics, cultural conflict, environmental conservation, and human health, Museum scientists conduct research in field locations across the globe and in state-of-the-art laboratories and computing and imaging facilities onsite. The Museum also plays a key role in training the next generation of scientists, including through the Richard Gilder Graduate School, the only museum-based Ph.D.-granting program in the Western Hemisphere.

Long a pioneer in museum education, in the 21st century the Museum, with its Gottesman Center for Science Teaching and Learning, is playing an increasingly formal role in improving science education, critical in an increasingly science- and technology-driven world. The Museum is building innovative programs, including powerful cross-sector partnerships that empower teachers and improve student achievement in science. One such model program is Urban Advantage, an unprecedented Museum-led partnership among eight New York City science institutions and the New York City Department of Education, now being replicated in cities across the nation. These formal programs join an array of fun, engaging, and inspiring learning opportunities for children, families, and the general public, from toddlers to seniors.

Firmly rooted in a deep tradition of science, education, and exhibition, the American Museum of Natural History is today a truly modern institution that brings a unique combination of resources and expertise to bear on the needs and opportunities of the 21st century. I invite you to enter our world and visit again and again—in this book, at the Museum itself, and online. I'm certain it will inform and inspire you.

Ellen V. Futter
President
American Museum of Natural History

TOP The Museum's iconic Central Park West façade—part of the Theodore Roosevelt Memorial, New York State's official memorial to its 33rd governor and the nation's 26th president—was restored in 2012.

BOTTOM LEFT The Rose Center for Earth and Space, which faces 81st Street, opened to the public in 2000 and increased the Museum's square footage by approximately 25 percent.

BOTTOM RIGHT The famous 77th Street "castle" façade, which was renovated in 2009, served as the Museum's main entrance from the late 1890s to the early 1930s.

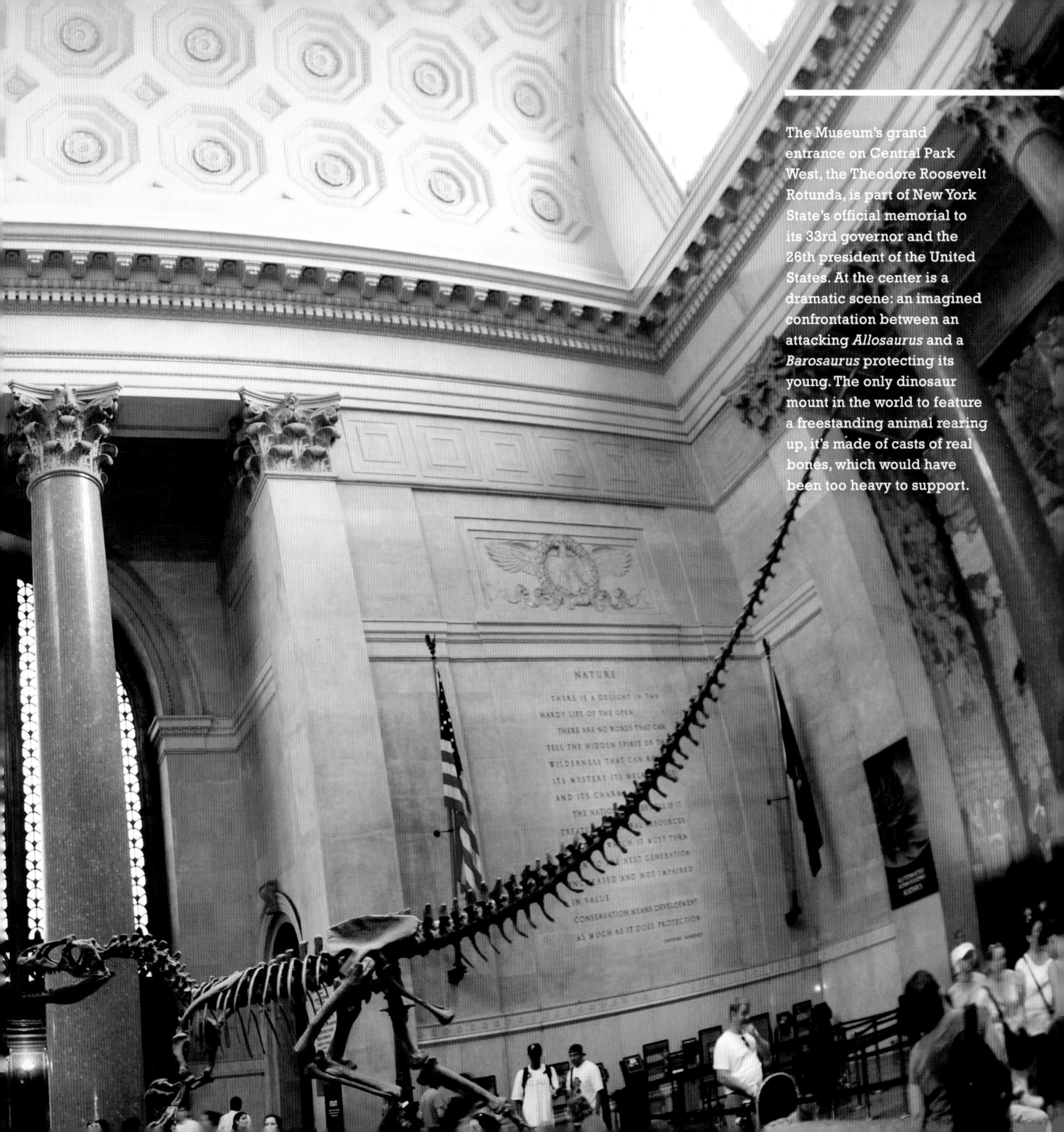

The Museum's grand entrance on Central Park West, the Theodore Roosevelt Rotunda, is part of New York State's official memorial to its 33rd governor and the 26th president of the United States. At the center is a dramatic scene: an imagined confrontation between an attacking *Allosaurus* and a *Barosaurus* protecting its young. The only dinosaur mount in the world to feature a freestanding animal rearing up, it's made of casts of real bones, which would have been too heavy to support.

MODERN MAMMALS

The moose is one of North America's largest living herbivores. Before the mass extinction of the continent's mammals 10,000 years ago, roughly two dozen species of plant-eating mammals were even larger.

AKELEY HALL OF

AFRICAN MAMMALS

A great bull elephant threatens, its trunk raised in the savanna twilight. Around his herd, 28 windows capture the continent's wildlife in freeze-frame, from hippos wallowing in the Nile to wildebeest grazing on the Serengeti.

Aesthetically and technically groundbreaking when it opened in 1936, this hall remains one of the great museum displays of the world. It commemorates Carl Akeley, the taxidermist, inventor, explorer, conservationist, sculptor, and nature photographer who first conceived of the hall in 1909 and collected many of its specimens. Each diorama re-creates a specific site at a particular time of day—every leaf and feather in place, every rock and ray of light carefully designed. Based on the meticulous observations of scientists in the field and of the artists and photographers who accompanied them, the dioramas vividly reproduce the worlds that Akeley loved and sought to preserve. He convinced King Albert of Belgium to create Africa's first national park, which includes the location depicted in the mountain gorilla diorama. It was here, on his fifth expedition to the site, that Akeley died and was buried.

TOP Carl Akeley was among the first to accurately document mountain gorillas as intelligent and social animals. Older, silver-backed males dominate family groups like this one, which spend the day slowly moving through dense forests. During the 20th century the lowlands in the background were transformed by farming and other human activity.

BOTTOM When the Museum's Lang-Chapin Congo Expedition set sail for Africa in 1909, the white rhino was already rare. This massive herbivore actually has a dark gray hide. Also known as the square-lipped rhinoceros, its name comes from the Dutch "weit" (wide), in reference to the animal's wide muzzle.

OPPOSITE Akeley revolutionized taxidermy. Instead of stuffing animal skins with straw or wood shavings, he fit them over realistic sculptures and placed them in groups in natural settings.

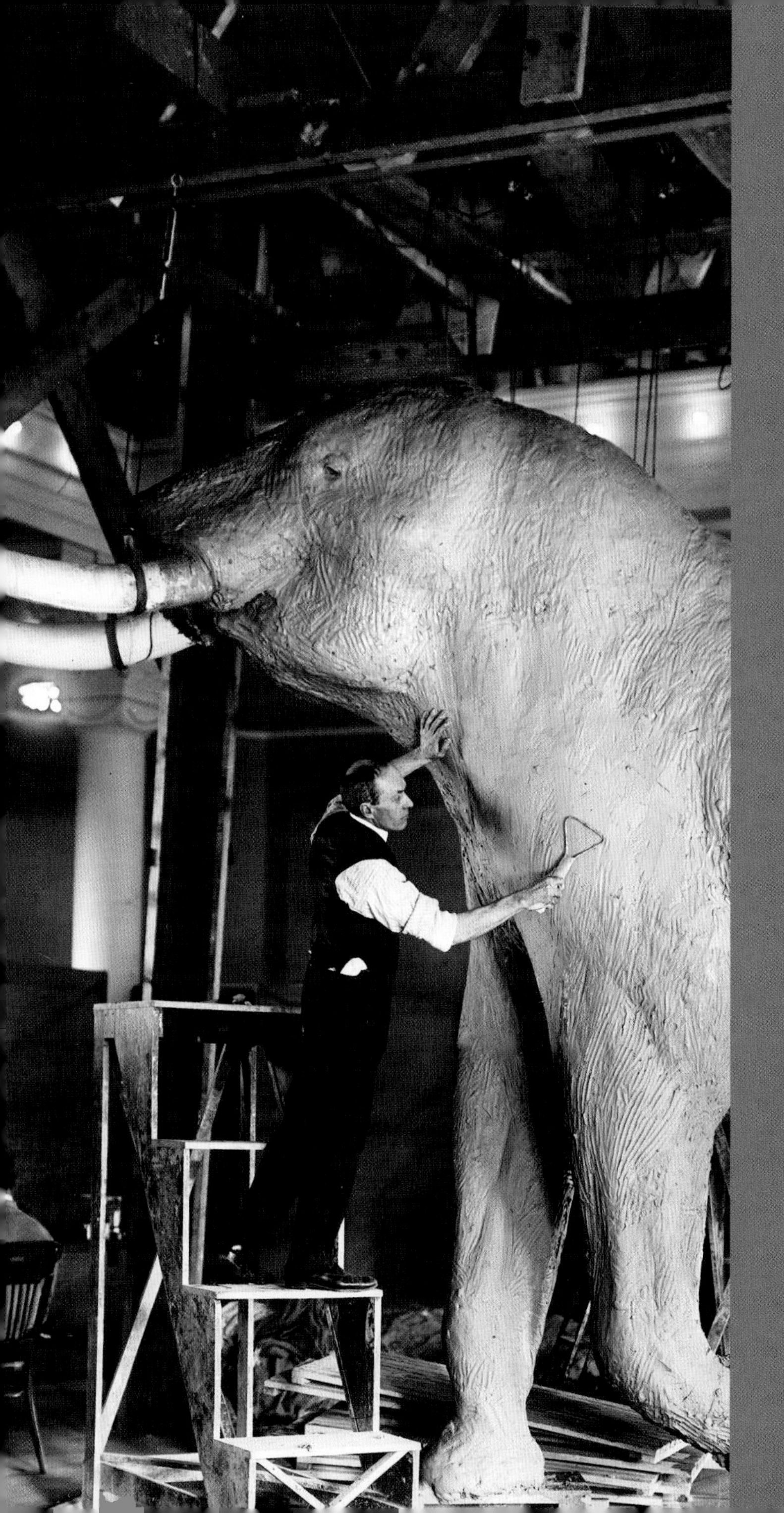

EXPEDITIONS

A century of scientific explorations, such as the one to the Belgian Congo where the above picture of Carl Akeley was taken, laid the foundation for diorama halls like this one. The tradition is going strong today. The Museum is base camp for more than 100 expeditions a year, including recent forays to Madagascar's Marojejy Mountains to collect rare chameleons; Gujarat, India, where insects trapped in amber are evidence that island chains may have once connected the subcontinent to Asia; the Mongolian valley of Ukhaa Tolgod, where rich fossil beds have produced scores of dinosaur skeletons and thousands of ancient mammal and lizard specimens; and the tiny Pacific atoll of Palmyra, to monitor how healthy coral reefs recover from disturbance. These expeditions yield specimens that build collections, answer questions, and pose new ones—enticing Museum scientists to set off across swamp, desert, glacier, and tropical sea once again.

JILL AND LEWIS BERNARD FAMILY HALL OF

NORTH AMERICAN MAMMALS

Even behind glass, the towering Alaska brown bear evokes a shiver, as do the majestic peaks that loom behind it.

The shimmering mountain range is the work of Museum artist and ardent conservationist Belmore Brown, who also painted the background of the Dall sheep diorama and helped establish the wildlife refuge known today as Denali National Park. The finest examples of background art in the Museum, this hall's habitat dioramas evoke the feel of the real places they depict, which range from a luminous snowfall in the Canadian Arctic to a sunset in the Sonoran Desert, and include scenes from Yellowstone, Yosemite, and Crater Lake National Parks. Also remarkable is their level of detail: notice the way the tracks of a panicked deer pick up speed as two wolves give chase under Minnesota's northern lights in the wolf diorama. The snow is made of crushed stone, the shadows a deft dusting of powdered pigment. First opened in 1942 with ten dioramas, the hall added others after a wartime hiatus. A total of 43 offer a spectacular record of North America's natural heritage. Restoring them to their original splendor was central to the 2011–12 conservation of this iconic hall.

TOP One labor-intensive conservation task was restoring the faded fur of the hall's bison, bears, coyotes, pronghorn, and elk back to their original hues. It took Museum specialists 15 days to formulate the seven colors used on the bison alone.

BOTTOM LEFT This photograph shows James Perry Wilson on location in Wyoming, painting a study for the background of the bison diorama. This was the largest of the 38 Museum dioramas he painted. A self-taught artist, Wilson perfected a grid system for achieving precise perspective within the curve of a diorama's rear wall.

BOTTOM RIGHT Tissue from threatened and endangered North American species collected by the United States National Park Service is housed in the Museum's Ambrose Monell Collection for Molecular and Microbial Research. This repository of the continent's biodiversity contains 60,000 specimens frozen in liquid-nitrogen–cooled vats at temperatures below –150° Celsius.

HALL OF

ASIAN MAMMALS

To create this hall's 12 dioramas, Museum taxidermists used the revolutionary methods developed by Carl Akeley for the Akeley Hall of African Mammals.

A pair of elephants stands at the center, inviting visitors to compare them to their larger African counterparts next door. Around them, a leopard rests, its paw draped across a peafowl's iridescent plumage; Hoolock gibbons swing from branch to branch; a majestic sambar, bloodied foot aloft, fends off a pack of wild dogs (opposite).

Much has changed since 1928, when Museum trustee Arthur S. Vernay and British colonel John C. Faunthrope made the last of "six expeditions into India, Burma, and Siam" to collect these specimens. Today, poaching and habitat loss gravely threaten many of the species represented here. Two examples of Asian mammals, the Siberian tiger and the giant panda, were among the animals relocated to the Endangered Species case when the Hall of Biodiversity opened in 1998. Working to protect these species and their habitats—and others in increasing jeopardy around the globe—is a central part of the Museum's mandate.

OPPOSITE LEFT Several floors above this leopard diorama, Museum scientists working in conservation genetics sequence big-cat DNA and design conservation management plans for endangered species that include leopards, snow leopards, tigers, lions, and jaguars. The state-of-the-art facilities are part of the Museum's Sackler Institute for Comparative Genomics.

OPPOSITE RIGHT Since 1998, the Museum's Center for Biodiversity and Conservation has been working with Vietnamese scientists and officials to identify and safeguard some of the country's endemic species. These include one of the world's most endangered primates, the grey-shanked douc, shown here at a rescue center in Vietnam.

HALL OF

PRIMATES

More than 300 primate species—including humans, monkeys, lemurs, and apes—are alive today, and all evolved from a common ancestor over the last 60 to 80 million years.

Primates range in size from the pygmy marmoset to the gorilla. Some live primarily in trees, and others on the ground; some are insect-eaters while others live on fruit, leaves, and sap. We humans share a number of traits with most of these relatives: large brains relative to body size, grasping hands, long lifespans, keen eyesight, and complex social groups. But apes, including humans, do not have tails, while most monkeys have long ones. Divided into families, the Hall of Primates uses skeletons, mounted specimens, and artwork to trace both shared traits and those unique to each group. Visitors can use various characteristics—including posture, amount of body hair, and shape of hand and thumb—to explore our relationship to this intriguing crowd of cousins.

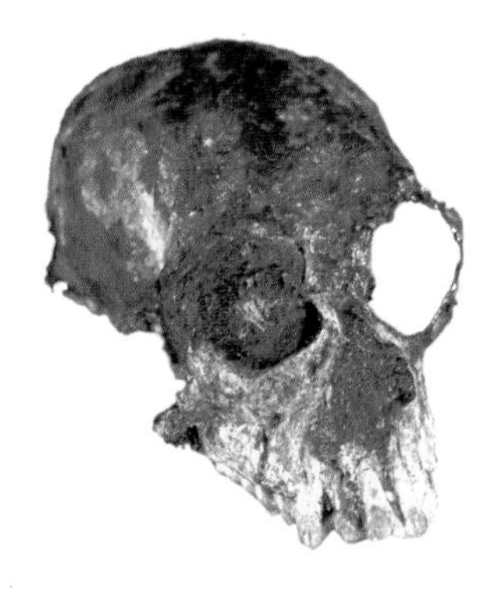

ABOVE In 1994, high in the Chilean Andes, Museum paleontologists and colleagues uncovered this skull of *Chilecebus*. Dating to 20 million years ago, it is the oldest and most complete well-dated primate skull from the Americas. South America was home to a remarkable menagerie of extinct mammals.

LEFT Primates are closely related and genetically similar to one another. On average, human DNA is 96 percent identical to the DNA of our most distant primate relatives, 97 percent identical to orangutans (left), and and nearly 99 percent identical to that of our closest relatives, chimpanzees and bonobos.

FOSSILS

Tyrannosaurus rex's pointed, knifelike teeth were ideal for slicing flesh. A joint midway through the lower jaw may have helped absorb the shock generated by struggling prey.

HALL OF

VERTEBRATE ORIGINS

This hall describes the journey of our extended vertebrate family from water onto land, an evolutionary sequence that stretches back more than 500 million years.

The first vertebrates were jawless fishes whose braincases and backbones helped them move, feed, and survive in an aquatic environment. Additional physical characteristics, basic yet revolutionary, enabled them to move onto land about 360 million years ago. Jaws made it easier to catch prey; limbs enabled walking, climbing, and many other kinds of movement; and watertight eggs made it possible to reproduce without returning to the water. Since then, vertebrates have evolved body forms that range from hummingbirds to hippopotamuses, and have adapted to almost every habitat on Earth. This hall's 250 fossil specimens represent almost every vertebrate group that has ever lived, including different groups of fishes; amphibians and their extinct early relatives, the first to walk on land; crocodiles, turtles, lizards, and snakes, the living descendants of the first animals to live entirely on land; giant sea creatures such as plesiosaurs, mosasaurs, and ichthyosaurs; and pterosaurs, the first flying vertebrates.

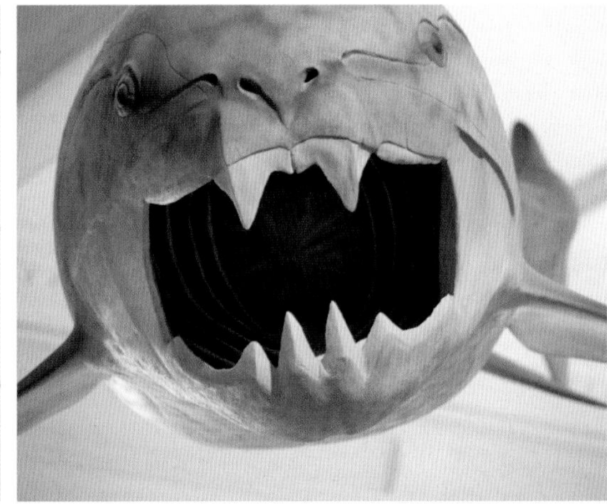

OPPOSITE TOP Pterosaur bones, like those of modern birds and their dinosaur ancestors, were hollow and filled with air. These light bones, coupled with large wingspans, enabled these reptiles to become the first vertebrates with truly powered flight.

OPPOSITE LEFT *Tylosaurus* was a large mosasaur, a marine lizard that lived during the Late Cretaceous and became extinct at the same time as non-avian dinosaurs. Double rows of teeth, flippers for steering, and a long, powerful tail made it a fearsome predator. This 28-foot (8.5-meter)-long skeleton was collected in 1899 in Hell Creek, Smoky Hill River, Kansas.

OPPOSITE RIGHT One of the first jawed vertebrates and one of the largest of the armored fishes called placoderms, *Dunkleosteus* was an aggressive predator. Serrated jawbones regenerated as they were worn down, and stayed razor-sharp by rubbing against the opposing blade.

RIGHT The fourth-floor fossil halls are laid out according to evolutionary relationships. Branching points mark evolutionary innovations, such as four limbs, or hooves, that a group of animals has in common. Called cladistics, this method of grouping organisms according to shared features was pioneered by Museum scientists.

DAVID H. KOCH DINOSAUR WING
HALL OF

SAURISCHIAN DINOSAURS

The fourth-floor elevator button is always lit, because that's where the dinosaurs are—the Museum's biggest attraction and just a tiny fraction of the largest collection of dinosaurs in the world.

Reflecting the most current thinking on dinosaur traits, behavior, and evolutionary links to birds, the Hall of Saurischian Dinosaurs examines the groups of dinosaurs that evolved from an ancestor with grasping hands. It features some of the Museum's most beloved and terrifying specimens, including *Tyrannosaurus rex* and *Apatosaurus* (formerly known as *Brontosaurus*). When the dinosaur halls were remodeled in the 1990s, *Apatosaurus* got a new skull and a longer, elevated tail, while *T. rex* was reconfigured from a "Godzilla" position to a low, stalking pose. Its 66-million-year-old bones—mostly real, like 85 percent of the fossils on display—come primarily from a specimen discovered in Montana by the Museum's legendary dinosaur-hunter Barnum Brown in 1908. Another famous contributor was naturalist and explorer—and, later, Museum director—Roy Chapman Andrews, whose expeditions to the Gobi Desert in the 1920s uncovered historic fossils of dinosaurs and early mammals.

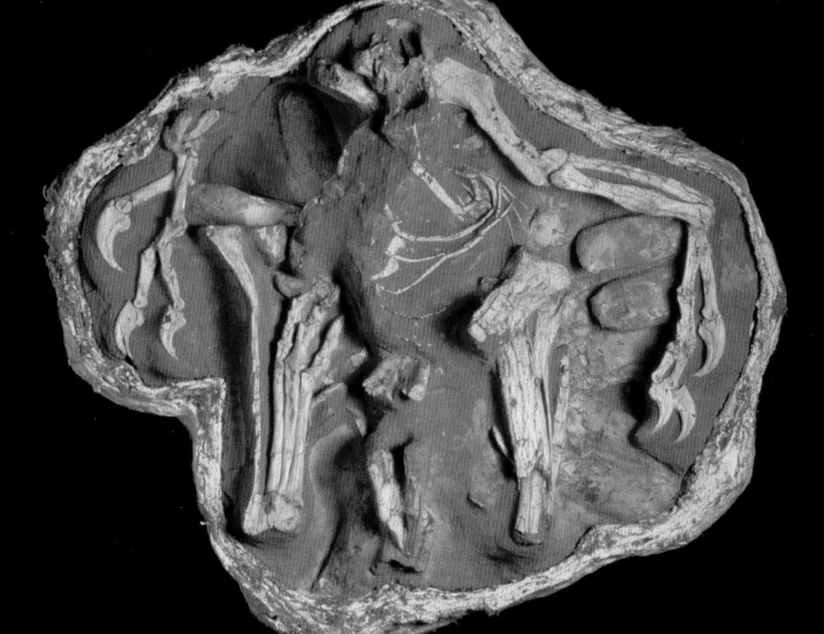

TOP Thanks to new fossil discoveries and research into topics like bone growth and biomechanics, scientists know more about tyrannosaurs than almost any other group of dinosaurs—even more than is known about some groups of organisms alive today. A specimen recently uncovered in northeastern China suggests that tyrannosaurs, including this ferocious *Tyrannosaurus rex*, were covered with fluffy proto-feathers at some stage in their lives.

BOTTOM In 1923, in the red sands of Mongolia's Flaming Cliffs, a lab technician named George Olsen found fossils that made headlines around the world: the first well-documented clutches of fossil dinosaur eggs. The animal by the nest was named *Oviraptor,* or "egg robber." It took 70 years to clear its reputation, when another Mongolian find by Museum scientists established that some dinosaurs brooded their eggs like modern birds and that the nest was *Oviraptor*'s own.

OPPOSITE Resourceful, physically strong, and always impeccably dressed, paleontologist Barnum Brown sent more than 1,200 crates of fossils back to the Museum from far-flung expeditions. No fewer than 57 of his spectacular specimens still mesmerize visitors today.

BIG BONE ROOM

The Museum's world-class vertebrate paleontology collection contains around 1 million specimens of which only a small fraction—0.02 percent—is on view at any time. The rest is stored behind the scenes in spaces like the aptly named Big Bone Room pictured above. Its largest holding is the 650-pound (295-kilogram) thighbone of the long-necked, plant-eating dinosaur *Camarasaurus*. Most of the bones are too large or too fragile to be displayed, but they're available for research purposes to paleontologists who come to the Museum from around the world.

DAVID H. KOCH DINOSAUR WING
HALL OF

ORNITHISCHIAN DINOSAURS

Completely renovated in the 1990s, the Museum's fossil halls now stand as a continuous loop that tells the story of vertebrate evolution.

Instead of placing exhibits in chronological order, the halls on the fourth floor are laid out as a family tree. Called cladistics, this approach groups animals according to shared physical characteristics. For ornithischian dinosaurs, this characteristic is a backward-pointing pelvic bone. The two stars of this hall are *Stegosaurus*, a 140-million-year-old dinosaur with bony plates embedded along its back (in addition to a cast of the only juvenile *Stegosaurus* ever found), and the 66-million-year-old, three-horned *Triceratops*. Much about these ancient creatures remains hotly debated: were they solitary or social, cold- or warm-blooded, smart or slow-witted? In their labs and collection rooms, scientists in the Division of Paleontology employ cutting-edge technologies in search of the answers.

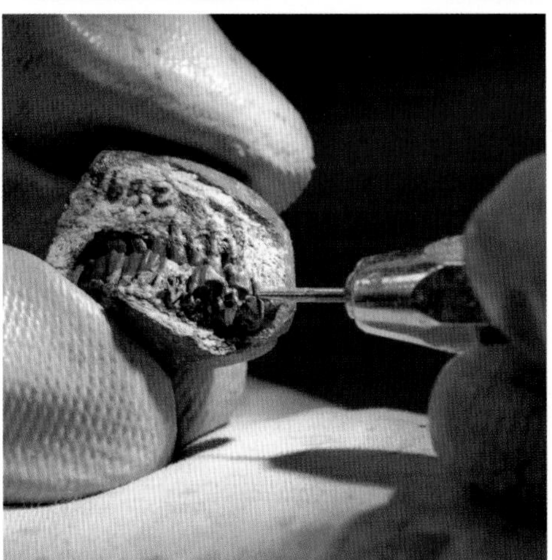

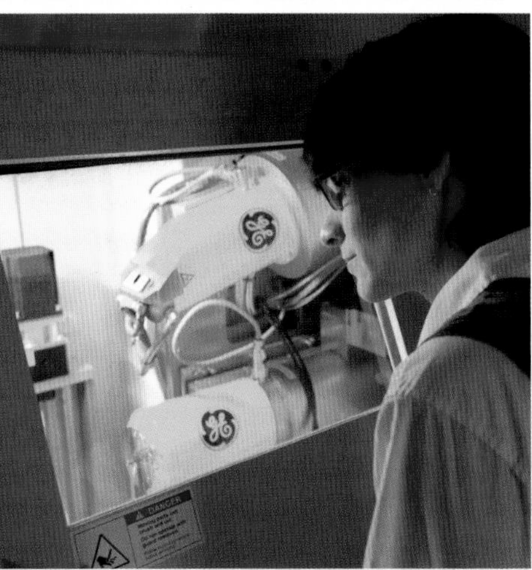

TOP This remarkable specimen, a duck-billed dinosaur from Canada named *Edmontosaurus,* is called a "mummy" because it left impressions of its soft tissues in the surrounding rock. It offers a rare glimpse into what dinosaur skin must have looked and felt like.

BOTTOM LEFT In the Fossil Prep Lab on the Museum's fifth floor, dexterous and patient preparators use tiny tools and modern glues and solvents to extract delicate specimens from the surrounding rock so that they can be studied.

BOTTOM RIGHT The Museum's computed tomography (CT) scanner is used to generate high-resolution images of objects, from fossil finds to anthropological artifacts, to see inside the item without damaging it.

LILA ACHESON WALLACE WING OF MAMMALS
AND THEIR EXTINCT RELATIVES
HALL OF

PRIMITIVE MAMMALS

This hall traces the lower branches of the mammalian evolutionary tree, which includes some of the most intriguing creatures on Earth: sloths, armadillos, opossums, kangaroos, and egg-laying echidnas and platypus.

This story of great diversifications and sudden extinctions began with lizardlike creatures with giant "sails" along their backs that dominated the planet millions of years before dinosaurs existed. They were known as synapsids, after the name of a large hole behind the eye socket, a key feature shared by mammals. By 200 million years ago, many mammals had evolved, but few got much larger than small rodents. Following the extinction of the large dinosaurs, they swiftly multiplied in number and in form, as demonstrated by the hall's striking assortment of fossil skeletons: wombat and giant ground sloth, glyptodont and saber-toothed cat, tiny shrew and *Indricotherium*, the largest land mammal known to have ever lived. Their relatives would evolve to swim, burrow, hop, climb trees, even fly—and to unearth this remarkable narrative.

ABOVE Found in 2011 by a Museum paleontologist, this fossil mammal from the Mesozoic contains clear and long-sought-after evidence of a defining evolutionary transition as reptiles gave rise to mammals. Over time, the multiple jawbones of reptiles grew smaller, moved upward, and became the bones that transmit sound vibrations in mammalian ears.

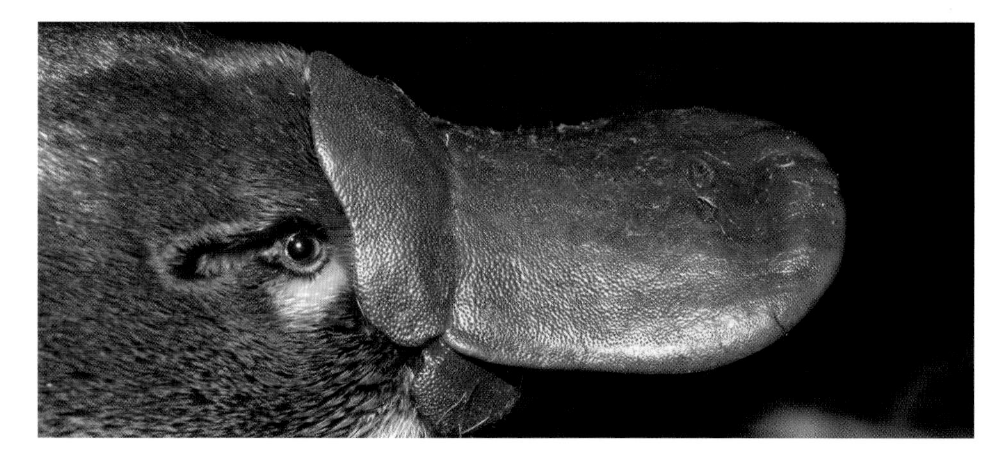

BOTTOM Some living animals that have certain primitive features, like the egg-laying mammal platypus, are called "living fossils." Charles Darwin coined the term in his book *On the Origin of Species*.

LILA ACHESON WALLACE WING OF MAMMALS AND THEIR EXTINCT RELATIVES
PAUL AND IRMA MILSTEIN HALL OF

ADVANCED MAMMALS

The dinosaurs may be the stars of the fossil halls, but the Museum's tradition of studying ancient mammals came first, and its collection of fossil mammals is the largest in the world.

Collecting began with an 1877 expedition to Wyoming's Bridger Basin. In 1895, before its scientists had excavated a single dinosaur, the Museum opened a full-scale hall of fossil mammals. This original hall is now part of the Lila Acheson Wallace Wing of Mammals and Their Extinct Relatives, which features mammals that arose after the extinction of the nonavian dinosaurs. Evolutionary branches are represented by cats, seals, bears, primates, horses, whales, and elephants. Large mammals like mammoths, mastodons, saber-toothed cats, camels, and giant ground sloths roamed across North America until about 10,000 years ago, when they died out over the course of a few centuries. Theories about what caused their extinction range from dramatic climate changes to a disease epidemic to hunting by humans.

OPPOSITE The hall's great standing skeleton belongs to a specimen of *Mammuthus*, a mammoth that was collected in Indiana and lived about 11,000 years ago. The famous woolly mammoth, known as *Mammuthus primigenius*, lived in Eurasia and North America and still inhabited remote islands in and around the Bering Strait when the Great Pyramid of Egypt was built 3,700 years ago. Genetic material from woolly mammoth remains is being studied by Museum scientists.

RIGHT One of the oldest known primatelike mammals, *Plesiadapis cookei*, lived in North America and Europe some 56 million years ago. It's a close relative of the group called euprimates, or "true" primates, to which lemurs, tarsiers, monkeys, and apes belong.

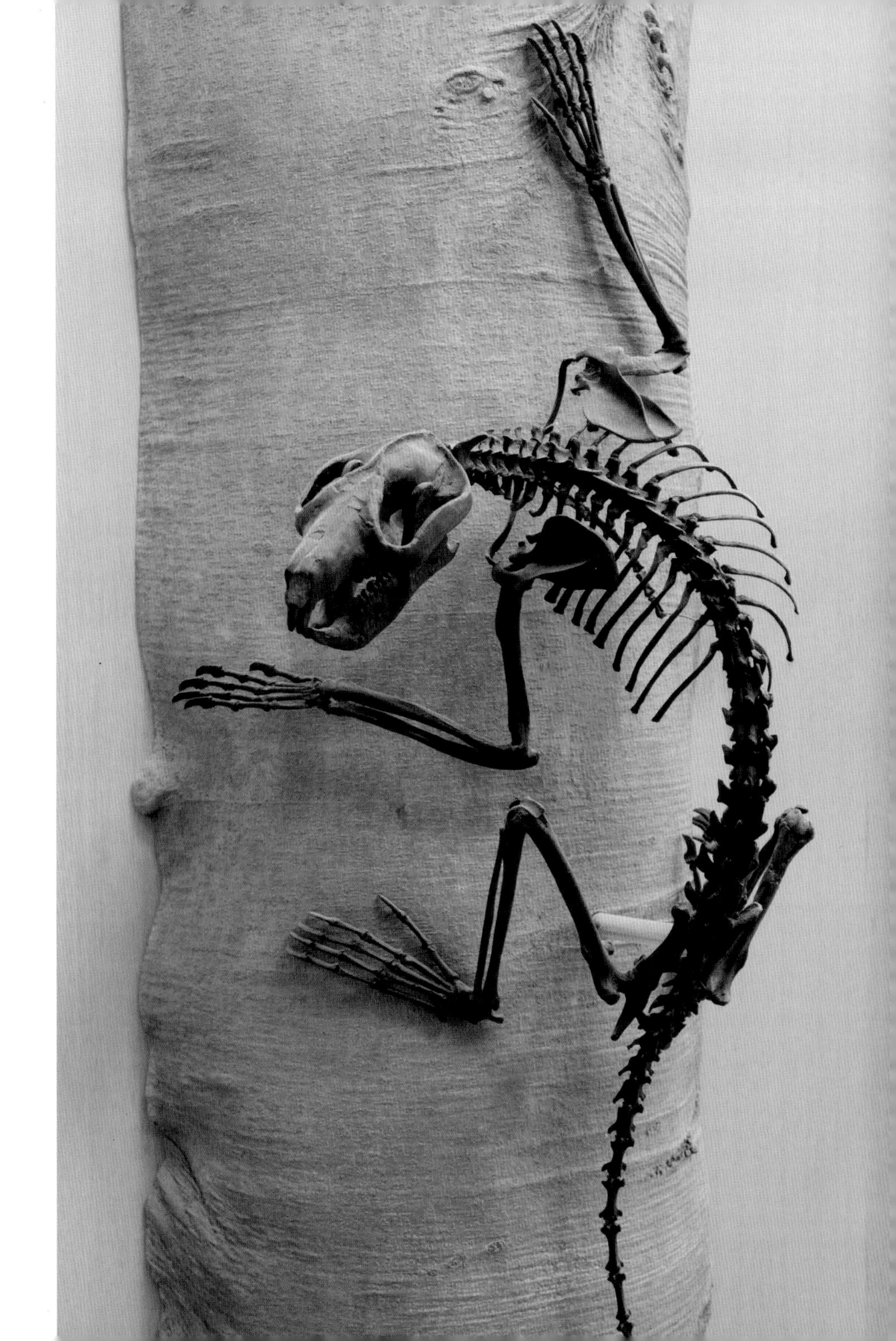

BIRDS, REPTILES, AND AMPHIBIANS

During the breeding season both male and female great egrets sport lacelike feathers, which were prized by 19th-century commercial plume-hunters. Museum ornithologist Frank Chapman helped put an end to the widespread use of feathers in ladies' hats, and egret populations have since rebounded.

LEONARD C. SANFORD HALL OF

NORTH AMERICAN BIRDS

When it opened in 1902, this hall was the first space in the world devoted to what are now called habitat dioramas.

It was created by ornithologist Frank M. Chapman, whose grasp of the power of the diorama paved the way for millions of Museum visitors to lose themselves in these engaging windows into the natural world. Most of the dioramas in this hall portray places where bird species were threatened by habitat loss and hunting, and one shows the now-extinct Labrador duck. A forceful advocate for conservation, Chapman popularized bird-watching in the United States and established the Christmas Bird Count, in which tens of thousands of birders around the world now participate. Under his direction, the Museum's bird collection grew to become one of the world's greatest, and it now holds 99 percent of all known species. Chapman traveled an estimated 90,000 miles (144,840 kilometers) to various sites depicted in this hall, which displays birds from Alaska to the Bahamas swimming, squawking, soaring, courting, hunting, and settling on their nests. He had only to cross the Hudson River to witness the scene depicted in one iconic diorama, in which a peregrine falcon delivers a pigeon to its three hungry chicks.

TOP Located high in Arizona's Chiricahua Mountains, the Museum's Southwestern Research Station is both a year-round field station for scientists and students and a prime destination for bird-watchers. Some 265 bird species have been recorded in the area, including over 13 species of hummingbirds as well as many birds migrating from Central and South America.

BOTTOM LEFT Housed in the Museum's Department of Ornithology, the Lewis B. and Dorothy Cullman Research Facility is a state-of-the-art laboratory for molecular systematics, the use of genetic information to study evolutionary relationships between organisms. Systematics research can have important conservation implications. For example, research by a Museum ornithologist established that Californian, northern, and Mexican spotted owls were distinct subspecies that merited separate conservation measures.

BOTTOM RIGHT Bird walks led by Museum experts are extremely popular, especially during the spring and fall migratory seasons. Here bird-watchers learn from an experienced Museum naturalist how to use field marks, habitat, behavior, and song to identify birds.

HALL OF

BIRDS OF THE WORLD

A few bird species are found worldwide, but most have adapted to a particular region—sometimes in remarkable ways.

Each of this hall's 12 dioramas depicts a biome—a region with a particular community of living things, such as tundra or tropical rain forest—and the enormous variety of birds that inhabit it. The grasslands and marshes of Argentina's pampas, for example, host waterbirds, insect-eaters, and seed-eaters, while Australia is home to fruit-loving parrots and cockatoos as well as the flightless emu, which can go for weeks without food. Swans and geese linger by the Gobi Desert's shallow Tsagaan Nuur lake. King penguins huddle on frigid South Georgia Island, near Antarctica. Massive wings spread, a condor comes in for a landing in the High Andes. Preparing these dioramas was not without incident. While field sketching for the tundra diorama in Churchill, Manitoba, Museum artist Frederick Scherer was stalked by wolves, which retreated only when he refused to. The Museum's Department of Ornithology maintains almost a million bird specimens, including skeletons, tissue samples, eggs, nests, and more than 800,000 skins, organized in trays that occupy six floors.

LEFT Each year on Identification Day, hundreds of visitors bring in bits of the natural world—shells and rocks, feathers and bones, flea market finds and exotic souvenirs—to be identified by Museum scientists. You show; they tell.

RIGHT Almost all of the major groups of birds, such as parrots, doves, and owls, arose within a few million years of each other around 60 million years ago, so few intermediate forms exist to connect them. Ornithologists at the Museum are hard at work on this puzzle.

HALL OF

REPTILES AND AMPHIBIANS

Reptiles are more closely related to mammals than amphibians. But historically they've been studied together because of how they were collected and stored, by preserving specimens in liquid.

In 1869, the year it was founded, the Museum acquired the natural history collection of German explorer Prince Alexander Philipp Maximilian, which included remarkable South American snakes and frogs. During the early 20th century, the size of the collection doubled to 110,000 specimens, some of which were cast in wax for display in the original Hall of Reptile and Amphibian Life. Displaying amphibians to the right of the aisle and reptiles to the left, today's hall compares and explains the biology of reptiles and amphibians in their full diversity. Exhibits range from tiny poison dart frogs to giant tortoises and Komodo dragons, one devouring a wild boar while another senses chemicals in the air with its long, forked tongue. With a collection of 350,000 specimens and active programs in the Americas, Africa, and Asia, the Museum's Department of Herpetology is a major research center.

BOTTOM LEFT The Museum is the first in the Western Hemisphere to grant Ph.D. degrees through its Richard Gilder Graduate School. Students have access to unparalleled resources and facilities, including a computed tomography (CT) scanner. One of the Ph.D. candidates in the comparative biology program used it to image the bony plates of armor in the skin of the crag lizard *Pseudocordylus subviridis*.

BOTTOM RIGHT Wondering how to get bitten by a snake? Perhaps not, but just in case, handy step-by-step instructions in the form of a whimsical mini-diorama are tucked inside one of the snake cases.

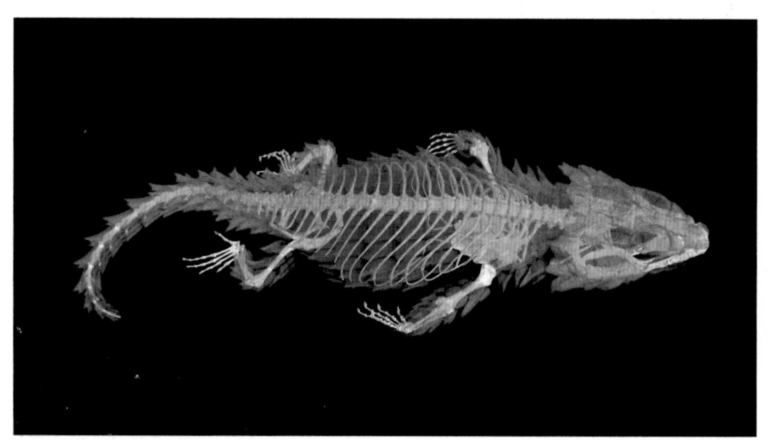

CHELICERATES

BIODIVERSITY AND CONSERVATION

The result of 3.5 billion years of evolution, the creatures in the Spectrum of Life exhibit range from microorganisms to terrestrial and aquatic giants and include bacteria, plants, fish, mammals, and insects. Interactive computer stations identify the specimens and explain their distribution on Earth.

THEODORE ROOSEVELT MEMORIAL HALL

Take a seat next to Theodore Roosevelt, sporting the rugged clothes he wore in Yosemite National Park two years into his presidency—possibly the most important camping trip in conservation history.

Together with the Museum's Central Park West façade and the Theodore Roosevelt Rotunda, this newly renovated hall is part of the official New York State Memorial to Theodore Roosevelt, the 26th president of the United States and the only one born in New York City. It uses specimens and interactive timelines to travel the arc of his life, from boyhood naturalist to avid hunter and on to the visionary conservationist who wrote, "Let us hope that the camera will largely supplant the rifle." A medallion at the center depicts a bison, a species whose near extinction impressed on Roosevelt the need to preserve and manage natural resources—a relatively new idea. Roosevelt listened closely to a circle of experts that included Museum curator Frank Chapman and naturalists John Burroughs and John Muir. It was Muir, on that camping trip, who urged the president to make Yosemite Valley part of a larger Yosemite National Park. Roosevelt went on to place some 230 million acres (930,777 square kilometers) under federal protection, including several places depicted in the Bernard Family Hall of North American Mammals. Motivated by the despoiling of Native American sites in the Southwest, he also signed into law the Antiquities Act of 1906. Used by many of Roosevelt's successors, the act now protects Palmyra Atoll, where scientists from the Museum's Center for Biodiversity and Conservation monitor coral reefs and sea turtle and seabird populations.

OPPOSITE LEFT Often ill as a child, Roosevelt studied natural history at home, learned taxidermy, and started his own collection. At age 12, he donated some of them—a dozen mice, a bat, a turtle, four birds' eggs, and the skull of a red squirrel—to the Museum. He collected and mounted this snowy owl in 1876, the same year he entered Harvard planning to become a naturalist, and gave it to the Museum in 1911.

OPPOSITE MIDDLE A bronze medallion depicts American bison grazing in Theodore Roosevelt National Park in the North Dakota Badlands. The inscription, from Roosevelt's Confession of Faith speech delivered at the Progressive National Convention in 1912, reads, "There can be no greater issue than that of conservation in this country."

OPPOSITE RIGHT Eleventh-century Chaco pots including this one were collected in the late 1800s from New Mexico's Chaco Canyon, a site now under the protection of the Antiquities Act of 1906. A century later, a new technology revealed that the urns once contained chocolate, a prized commodity that the Ancestral Pueblo peoples could have obtained only by trading with their Mesoamerican neighbors far to the south. The Museum has a remarkable collection of this elegant pottery.

HALL OF

BIODIVERSITY

Primates, Planet Earth, Pacific Peoples . . . we know what to expect inside those halls. Describing the variety, interdependence, and vulnerability of life on Earth is an entirely different challenge.

The Hall of Biodiversity is a visually and intellectually compelling response to this complex and urgent mandate. Along one side runs the luminous Spectrum of Life wall, where 1,500 specimens and models showcase the glorious diversity of life on Earth across 3.5 billion years of evolution. At the center, a walk-through diorama immerses visitors in the sights, sounds, and smells of one of Earth's richest ecosystems: a swath of Africa's Dzanga-Sangha rain forest, each of its 500,000 leaves detailed by hand by Museum artists. Behind the diorama, BioBulletin videos explain the effects on biodiversity of El Niño, habitat fragmentation, fires, and other current events. Human activities are driving Earth's sixth great extinction, a crisis depicted here along with conservation efforts around the world to restore and protect key ecosystems. The many Museum scientists who study the organization, distribution, and history of life on Earth know that biodiversity plays a critical role in sustaining life as we know it. The future is in our hands.

BOTTOM LEFT Each year, winners of the Young Naturalist Awards—a nationwide essay competition for students in grades 7 through 12 who conduct their own scientific research—are invited to the Museum for behind-the-scenes tours. Launched when the Hall of Biodiversity opened in 1998, the Young Naturalist Awards recognize investigations into topics like memory retention in honeybees and snapping turtle populations in the Bronx.

BOTTOM RIGHT In 1993, the Museum created the interdisciplinary Center for Biodiversity and Conservation. CBC research provides a scientific framework for the complex political and economic decisions needed to confront species extinction. Focused on areas where biodiversity is both rich and under threat, CBC partnerships include projects in the Bahamas, the Solomon Islands, and Vietnam, as well as in the New York metropolitan area.

BIRDS
CRUSTACEANS
TURTLES
SNAKES AND LIZARDS
CROCODILES AND BIRDS
MAMMALS
CHELICERATES
CRUSTACEANS

IRMA AND PAUL MILSTEIN FAMILY HALL OF

OCEAN LIFE

Floating in a "virtual ocean," a monumental model of a blue whale watches over an immersive representation of the largest habitable space on Earth, from sun-dappled reef to pitch-black abyss.

To land dwellers, the ocean might appear a homogenous blue expanse, but beneath the waves lies an amazing range of habitats that support an astonishing array of life. After all, life on Earth probably began in the ocean, most major groups stayed there, and some land animals—the ancestors of manatees, seals, sea lions, and whales—returned to it. Models of more than 750 sea dwellers depict this diversity, from a 14-foot (4-meter)-long whale shark to scarlet tube worms and tiny green bubble algae. Habitat dioramas provide portholes into key ocean ecosystems: estuaries, mangrove forests, polar seas, continental shelves, coral reefs, kelp forests, the dark midwater column, and the deep-sea floor. Flanking the entrance are models of the Tree of Life that show the evolution of marine organisms over the last 1.5 billion years, from a profusion of microscopic plants through the cartilaginous and bony fishes and including, on a relatively recent mammalian branch, a scuba diver.

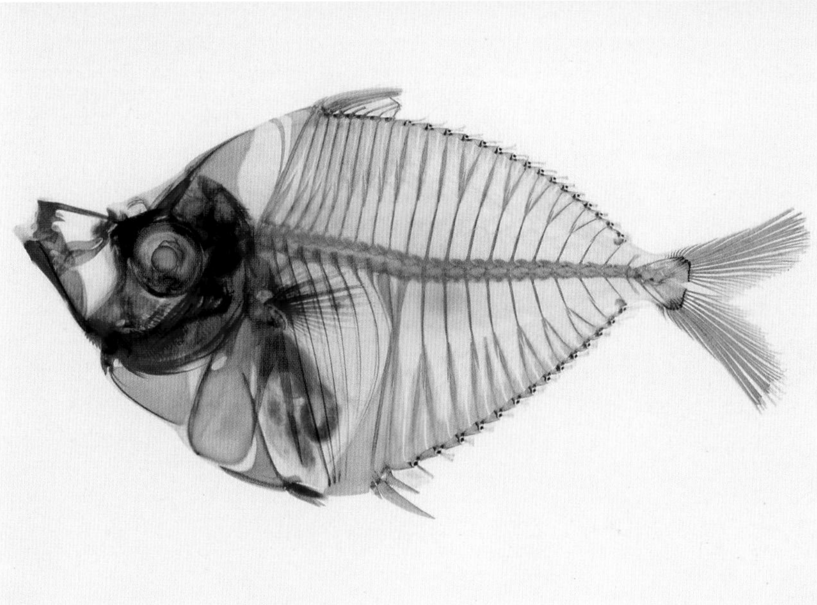

TOP This diorama depicts a giant squid battling a sperm whale. Researchers first captured a giant squid on camera in 2005, but most of our knowledge of these giant invertebrates comes from dead specimens. Sucker-size scars on the skin of sperm whales and indigestible squid beaks in their stomachs are good evidence that such deep-sea battles do occur, and that whales sometimes win.

BOTTOM Active research projects by scientists in the Museum's Department of Ichthyology include exploring the lower Congo River's fish biodiversity, describing a new species of rock-climbing catfish in Venezuela, and studying the signaling systems of bioluminescent ponyfishes, which live, like the one at bottom, off the coast of Madagascar.

OPPOSITE Once thought to be barren, the deep-sea floor teems with life around hydrothermal vents, where superheated, mineral-rich water gushes into the frigid darkness. A giant tubeworm can grow up to 8 feet (2.4 meters) long and 4 inches (10 centimeters) wide. Most of what you see is a hard tube that supports the worm's soft body and protects it from toxic chemicals and predators.

THE BLUE WHALE

In 1969, when this model was originally installed, man had walked on the Moon but had yet to study a living blue whale. Beating out models at the British Museum and the Smithsonian by several feet, this blue whale was a huge success. On the first Sunday after the new Hall of Ocean Life and Biology of Fishes opened, more than 35,000 visitors set a new Museum attendance record. Based on a dead female collected in 1925 off the southern tip of South America, this 94-foot (28.7-meter)-long fiberglass and polyurethane model weighs 21,000 pounds (9,525 kilograms). During the 2003 renovation of the hall, "cosmetic surgery" fixed the whale's bulging eyeballs, colored her more accurately, and added a navel—a small but significant modification considering that the model depicts the largest placental mammal ever to have lived. We still know remarkably little about these rare animals, which spend most of their time below the surface of the ocean and well out of our sight.

HALL OF

NORTH AMERICAN FORESTS

This hall explores the continent's splendid forests, from a stand of spruce and fir in northern Ontario to a desert of giant saguaro cacti in Arizona.

Its dioramas, which showcase the community of plants and animals that coexist in each habitat, have captivated not just schoolchildren but world-famous artists including photographer Hiroshi Sugimoto. One hall highlight is a slice of sequoia trunk that features historic markers—like one for Charlemagne's coronation in AD 800—which denote the 13 centuries during which the tree grew from sapling to colossus. Another highlight takes visitors across scale instead of time: a cross section of forest floor enlarged to 24 times its actual size, in which a massive millipede makes its way past an acorn the size of a bass drum. And there is the unnerving wax model of an *Anopheles* mosquito enlarged to 75 times actual size—a most effective way to alert the New York public to a dangerous outbreak of malaria in 1917–18, when it was first exhibited.

FELIX M. WARBURG HALL OF

NEW YORK STATE ENVIRONMENT

Focused on the seasonal and natural cycles of New York's Dutchess County, this hall highlights the rhythms of farm and forest and where the two meet.

The region is rich with mountains, natural lakes, woodlands, a variety of rock formations, as well as wildlife. Cutaway views of life below ground show a chipmunk hibernating atop a hoard of acorns and a toad crouched in a mole's burrow. By spring, the toad is back in the pond to mate, the chipmunk's nest is full of young, and a queen yellow jacket has taken over an empty mouse den for her colony.

Other exhibits depict the cadence of cultivation, including a look at a local apple orchard and life on a dairy farm. Since it opened in 1951, this hall has taught legions of local schoolchildren about the region's geological history, how different rock formations affect the soil, and how soils, in turn, shape the biodiversity and agriculture of this beautiful part of the Empire State.

HUMAN ORIGINS AND WORLD CULTURES

This is a detail of the 63-foot (19-meter)-long Great Canoe, which was carved from a single cedar tree by craftsmen from the First Nations of British Columbia. The canoe has been a Museum landmark since its arrival in 1883. It is displayed at the center of the restored Grand Gallery, recently renovated along with the famous 77th Street "castle" façade.

ANNE AND BERNARD SPITZER HALL OF

HUMAN ORIGINS

A Neanderthal skullcap discovered in 1856 was the first accepted proof that other kinds of humans once walked the Earth.

Since then, thousands of other fossils, representing many distinct species, have helped paleoanthropologists piece together the what, when, and where of our ancient ancestors. In the 1990s, geneticists joined the effort, using DNA to shed light on how modern humans are related to one another and what makes our species unique. Like the two strands of DNA's double helix, these two scientific threads—bones and genes—converge in the Spitzer Hall of Human Origins to describe the "family tree" of human evolution. Drawing on the Museum's long-standing mastery of the habitat diorama, life-size tableaux of daily life in prehistoric times remind us that our hominid ancestors were often prey, not predators. Specimens include a remarkable reconstructed Neanderthal skeleton, and striking reconstructions of "Lucy" and "Turkana Boy" reveal what these ancestors probably looked like. Panels in the final gallery discuss what may lie in store for our species. Embodying the pace-setting cross-disciplinary research under way across the Museum, this hall addresses in unprecedented depth the question of what it means to be human.

TOP This is the first Museum hall to house a hands-on teaching facility, the Sackler Educational Laboratory for Comparative Genomics and Human Origins. Regular classes for school groups and the general public use DNA and fossil evidence to explore hominid history.

BOTTOM A touch-screen display explains how paleoanthropologists, including Museum researchers, find fossils in the field.

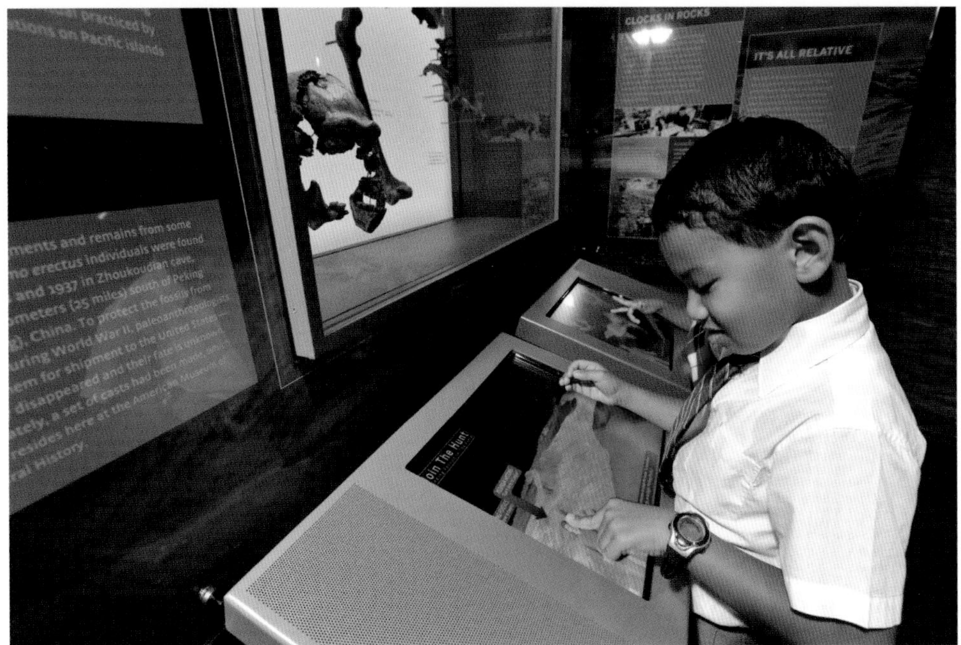

HALL OF

NORTHWEST COAST INDIANS

The Museum's oldest hall, this dramatic gallery showcases research conducted during the Jesup North Pacific Expedition (1897–1902), the most ambitious anthropological survey ever undertaken.

The Jesup Expedition was led by Museum curator Franz Boas, known as the father of modern anthropology for his pioneering work on race, culture, and language. Interested in determining whether the first Americans had crossed over an Arctic land bridge from Asia, he investigated cultural and biological links between peoples living in a giant arc along the Pacific coast from Siberia to northwestern North America. Traveling by boat and dogsled, expedition teams brought back over 11,000 objects, including boats, sleds, weapons, toys, clothing, and the massive totem poles that line the hall. They also observed social practices, collected data and artifacts, made wax cylinder recordings, and took thousands of photographs—an early example of the revolutionary use of the camera as an anthropological tool. Over a century later, the Museum returned some of these archival photographs to the communities where they were taken, as part of an ongoing dialogue with scholars and Native peoples of the Russian Far East.

ABOVE This unique feast dish with its detachable dorsal fin was used by the Kwakwaka'wakw Indians at a potlatch, or great ceremonial gathering. Part killer whale and part human, it commemorates a hero's magical journey to villages under the sea, escorted by killer whales. The dish was acquired by a field consultant to Franz Boas named George Hunt, who was half English and half Tlingit, raised as a Kwakwaka'wakw, and a linguist and ethnologist in his own right.

RIGHT Based in the Division of Anthropology, the Museum's Objects Conservation Lab surveys the Museum's collections for artifacts that require attention. During the recent conservation of totem poles displayed in this hall, including this house post, specialists used magnification and ultraviolet light to distinguish original surfaces from materials applied during earlier restoration efforts to help determine treatment.

HALL OF
EASTERN WOODLANDS INDIANS

Clothing like this elaborately embroidered deerskin coat, one of several intriguing garments featured in this hall, conveys a great deal about a culture's values and traditions.

This coat was sewn by the Iroquois, one of the many agricultural societies living in eastern North America when European settlers arrived in the 1600s. Made in the early 19th century, this European-style jacket is richly decorated with beadwork in floral patterns that reflect contact with British, French, and Dutch arrivals. Missionaries sometimes taught these motifs to the Indians, while traders and settlers introduced glass beads along with metal tools, firearms, and other goods. Some Iroquois helped spread these new materials and techniques as traders and partners in European commercial enterprises. After the Revolutionary War divided the Iroquois Confederacy, much tribal homeland was surrendered, although sizeable groups still remain in New York State, Ontario, and Québec. Among them are the skilled Mohawk ironworkers who have helped raise New York City's towering skyscrapers since the 1920s.

HALL OF

PLAINS INDIANS

Rather than adopt European motifs, the great hunters and horsemen of the North American Plains incorporated new materials into existing indigenous patterns.

Beads replaced porcupine quills in traditional geometric designs like the ones that decorate this 19th-century Dakota Sioux woman's outfit, which also includes ornaments made from dentalia shells obtained through trade with West Coast Indians. These militarily powerful Indian nations, which include the Blackfeet, Hidatsa, Dakota Sioux, Cheyenne, Arapaho, and Crow, remained at war with the new republic well into the 1890s. Pushed west, they became fully nomadic hunters who maintained a spectacular culture until the bison neared extinction. Museum anthropologists who studied and lived with the Native peoples of North America in the early 20th century exchanged cash and other desirable goods for some of the remarkable ethnographic pieces displayed in these halls.

MARGARET MEAD HALL OF

PACIFIC PEOPLES

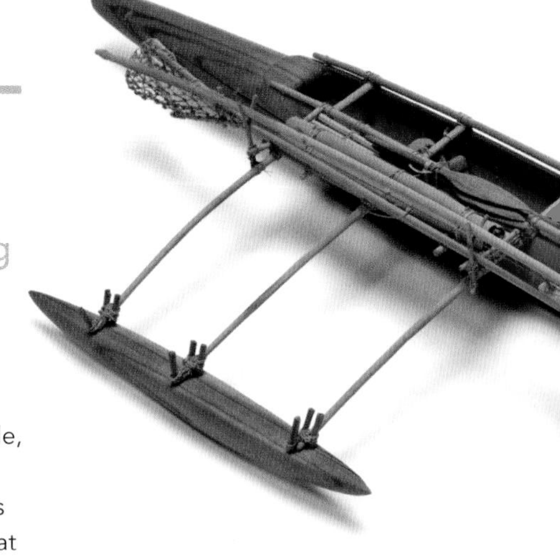

In 1928 anthropologist Margaret Mead published *Coming of Age in Samoa*, the best seller that introduced countless readers to the value of looking carefully and open-mindedly at other cultures.

Mead's fieldwork in the South Pacific is responsible for many of the objects in this hall, whose original design she developed. One prominent feature is the cast of a *moai* ancestor figure from Rapa Nui, also known as Easter Island—and familiar to many visitors from the movie *Night at the Museum*. Easter Island is just one of some 25,000 islands in the Pacific Ocean, which covers a third of the globe. About 10,000 islands are home to living cultures that integrate traditional skills and beliefs with modern life. For example, some of New Zealand's Māori people continue to make intricate woodcarvings like the ones that adorn a storehouse that is featured in the hall. Such storehouses represent the bodies of ancestors, which are central in most Pacific societies and inhabit the present and future as well as the past.

OPPOSITE TOP Outrigger canoes have long been used by Pacific Islanders; the second hull makes them much more stable. Recently added to the Museum's collection, this canoe model is from Tuvalu, an island midway between Hawaii and Australia.

OPPOSITE LEFT When Mead first began taking pictures, long before the video and digital revolutions, producing a satisfactory ethnographic film was a heroic enterprise. Since 1976, the Margaret Mead Film Festival has been the premiere showcase for international documentaries.

OPPOSITE RIGHT This spectacular cloak was worn by a Hawaiian chief, an important sacred figure. It was crafted by specialist feather gatherers and weavers from the feathers of as many as 80,000 birds.

RIGHT This cast of a *moai* ancestor figure was made on a 1935 Museum expedition to Rapa Nui.

GARDNER D. STOUT HALL OF

ASIAN PEOPLES

Befitting a landmass that stretches from the Arabian Peninsula to the Bering Straits and is home to some of the world's most populous countries, this is the Museum's largest cultural hall.

Each culture represented is unique, yet each incorporates elements of cross-cultural exchange: the movement of goods, religions, inventions, and people across deserts, mountains, and oceans. This hall focuses on the cultural practices of people observed by ethnographers at the time. This approach is exemplified by the shaman diorama, which re-creates a late-19th-century healing ceremony of the Yakut of eastern Siberia. Eminent anthropologist Berthold Laufer's many contributions to the Museum's exceptional Asian Ethnographic Collection include a set of Tibetan masks, including the one opposite, which are evidence of a multiethnic China at the turn of the 20th century. Museum researchers continue to add extraordinary artifacts, such as a full-size model of a Peugeot bicycle acquired in Vietnam in 2003. Made of paper, it is meant to be burned in a traditional funeral rite and reflects the way customs persist and adapt to global influences.

LEFT Museum researchers have been collecting paper votives—items made to be burned or buried at funerals—from Asia since the early 20th century. Early 21st-century versions range from bicycles, like this one, to electric rice cookers, cell phones, and laptop computers, and reflect rising economic aspirations for both the living and the dead.

HALL OF

AFRICAN PEOPLES

The exhibits in this hall, which include just a small percentage of more than 45,000 objects in the Museum's African collection, cover this massive continent in extraordinary depth.

From a cat mummified in Egypt some 3,500 years ago to the elaborate brass weights used to measure gold in Ghana's Asante society (top right), the collection is rich in objects of historical interest and daily life. Many were collected in multiple iterations that allow scholars to see how patterns and techniques developed and spread. The collection shows how objects can reveal information about the societies from which they come, and illuminates the process of conflict and assimilation that takes place when groups come into contact. Mancala games (like the one opposite), which do not require a shared language, are interesting examples of cultural transmission, and this hall contains four of them. One board that traveled from West Africa during the slave trade is in the African Peoples in the Americas section. Music, too, is a language of its own. The hall features recordings made during a Museum expedition to the Congo in the 1950s, and as visitors listen to these soundscapes, they can find some of the instruments on which the songs were played.

LEFT The elaborate contemporary costumes displayed in this hall are worn during initiation into Liberian secret societies, which link communities to their ancestors and deities.

RIGHT Much material from central Africa was collected in expeditions such as the Lang-Chapin Congo Expedition (1909–15). Ornithologist Herbert Lang and his assistant James Chapin returned with more than 4,000 objects, including insects and amphibians, carvings and textiles, musical instruments and tools, including this ivory and metal knife from Niangara.

HALL OF

MEXICO AND CENTRAL AMERICA

What's the best way to understand the Aztec, Mayan, and other great cultures of ancient Mesoamerica?

Through the anthropological discipline known as archaeology: studying the objects that past societies left behind, like those showcased in this hall. The Museum's extensive archaeological collection is the result of more than a century of ambitious fieldwork, which got its start in 1899 when the first hall dedicated exclusively to the archaeology of Mexico and Central America was founded. At the time, archaeology was just beginning to shed light on pre-Hispanic culture. Systematic excavations enabled archaeologists to show how culture changed over time and to compare different sites, while everyday items revealed pre-Hispanic ways of making music, waging war, and preparing food. These new data laid the groundwork for the concept of Mesoamerica: a region of shared cultures with their roots deep in antiquity and distinct from those to the north and south. This hall showcases astonishing artifacts from the Olmec, the Zapotec, the Maya, and the Aztec—whose grand cities in Mexico, Guatemala, and Honduras were centers of religion, politics, trade, and the arts until the Spanish conquest in 1521.

ABOVE This Zapotec urn, a ceramic vase depicting an anthropomorphic being, is from Oaxaca, Mexico, where Museum archaeologists have been active since 1898. Experts in the Museum's Objects Conservation Laboratory specialize in reconstructing these urns, which were often used for mortuary purposes.

ABOVE First described by mineralogist George Kunz in 1890, this sophisticated jade sculpture is 3,000 years old. The figure depicted is part human, part beast, and may represent a chief or shaman who has transformed himself into a jaguar.

ABOVE This beautiful mask made by the Tarahumara Indians was collected by Carl Lumholtz, a Museum researcher who lived among them in 1891. Used during celebrations, it was associated with supernatural beings that helped ensure good hunting. While the Hall of Mexico and Central America displays artifacts from the archaeological collection, the Museum's Mexican Ethnology Collection includes more than 5,000 objects from living cultures.

HALL OF

SOUTH AMERICAN PEOPLES

Stoneware, metalwork, shards of pottery . . . these are the traces of ancient societies that archaeologists tend to encounter. Textiles are rare.

Yet, in 1946, in a mound called Huaca Prieta on the Peruvian north coast, Dr. Junius Bird uncovered some of the oldest textile fragments ever found in the New World, dating back some 5,000 years. Painstakingly reconstructed under microscopes in a method pioneered at the Museum, the fragments demonstrate the sophisticated weaving and textile-making technology of pre-ceramic cultures. The Museum's curator for South American archaeology for 34 years, Bird recognized the central role of textiles as a medium of expression in ancient Andean culture, remarkable for their colors, figures, and motifs. An example is the cloak (opposite) made by the Paracas people (800–100 BC). Andean achievements in metallurgy were also extraordinary, and this hall showcases exquisite examples such as the Royal Llama of the Inka (top right), a 500-year-old silver figurine from Lake Titicaca, Bolivia. In addition to representing pre-Columbian cultures, the hall includes a section on Amazonia with tools, weapons, ceremonial objects, and spectacular featherwork on view.

BOTTOM LEFT This mask made by the Tapirapé people of the Brazilian Amazon represents the spirit of an enemy killed in battle. It was designed to be carried by a warrior during ceremonies.

BOTTOM RIGHT These dramatic ear ornaments are made from toucan feathers, glass beads, and the iridescent wing covers of the giant ceiba borer beetle, *Euchroma gigantea*. They're worn by men of the Shuar people of the upper Amazon for special occasions. Other examples of Shuar craftsmanship can be found in the hall, including a back ornament made from the wing covers of another colorful beetle, *Chrysophora chrysochlora*.

EARTH AND SPACE

The Hayden Sphere in the Rose Center for Earth and Space is supported by three huge steel legs, like a tripod, which enables visitors to walk under as well as all the way around it.

FREDERICK PHINEAS AND SANDRA PRIEST

ROSE CENTER FOR EARTH AND SPACE

Opened to the public in February 2000, the Rose Center for Earth and Space is one of the most ambitious projects in the history of the Museum.

It contains five exhibition spaces, including the Gottesman Hall of Planet Earth, the Cullman Hall of the Universe, the Heilbrunn Cosmic Pathway, and the Hayden Planetarium, and houses the Department of Astrophysics. Bathed in natural light, the spectacular seven-story structure is a research facility, an education center, and an architectural marvel. Its centerpiece is the luminous 2,000-ton (1,800-metric-ton) Hayden Sphere, which appears to float behind one of the largest suspended glass curtain walls in the United States—almost an acre (4,000 square meters) of astoundingly clear "water white" glass held together with 2.5 miles (4 kilometers) of rod rigging and 1,400 steel spiders. Organizing cosmic objects and phenomena around the physical principles that unite them, the Rose Center creates a seamless journey from the outer reaches of the universe to the inner workings of planet Earth.

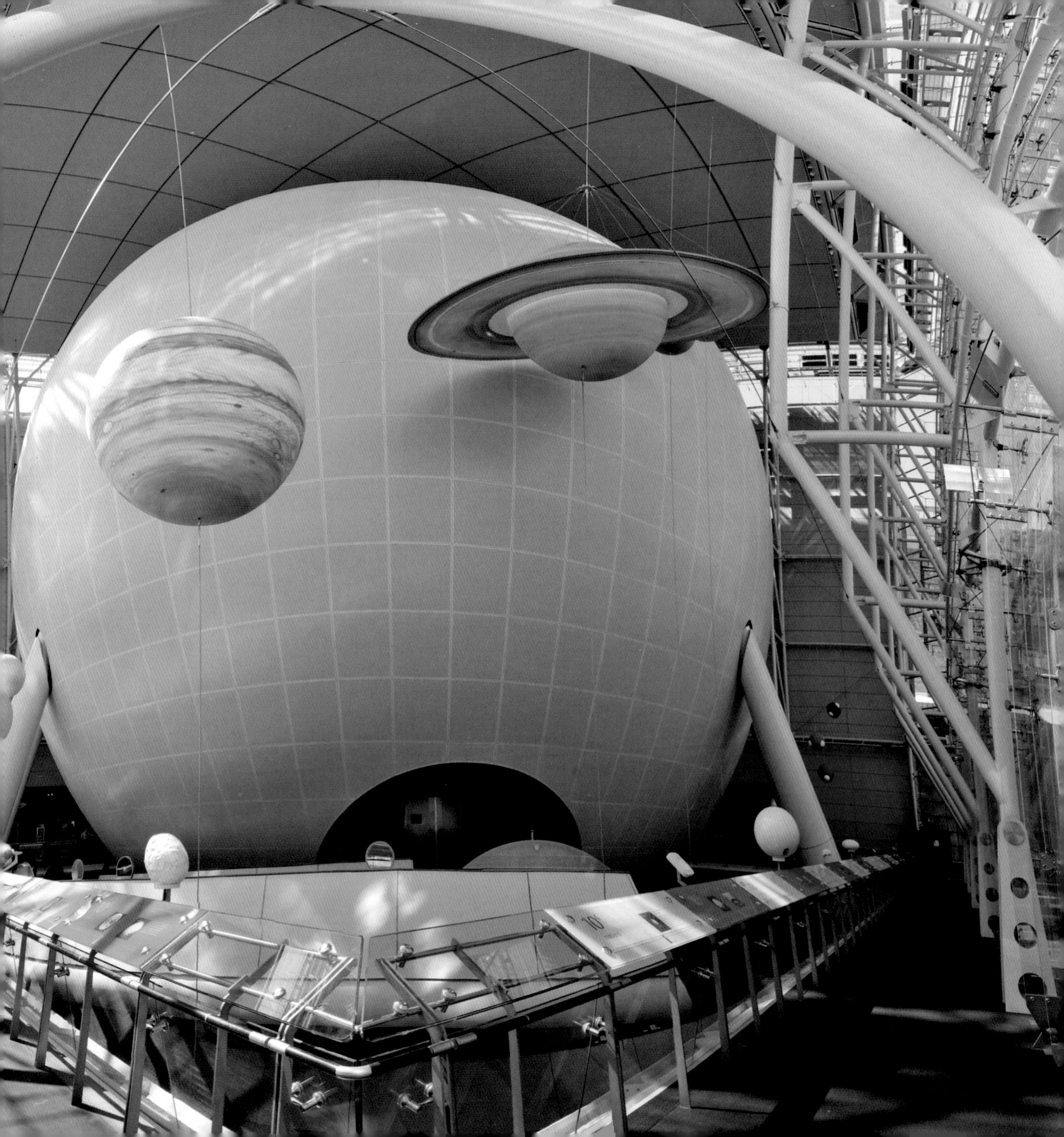

HAYDEN PLANETARIUM

Generations of New Yorkers first raced to space in the original Hayden Planetarium. Since its reopening in 2000, their children and grandchildren have traveled even farther—to the edge of the observable cosmos.

Housed in the top of the sphere, which seems to hover in the middle of the Rose Center for Earth and Space, the new planetarium is one of the largest and most powerful virtual reality simulators in the world. Using a cutting-edge projection system, Space Shows in the 429-seat theater draw on physics-based computer simulations and millions of actual astronomical observations to take visitors on a breathtaking journey through the observable universe: planets, star clusters, nebulae, and galaxies. This Digital Universe—a three-dimensional atlas of all astronomical objects whose distance from Earth is known—is maintained by Museum astrophysicists. Not just an extraordinary exhibition, the Hayden Planetarium builds upon the distinguished educational legacy established by its beloved predecessor.

BOTTOM LEFT The first Hayden Planetarium was built in 1935. Its mission, in the words of philanthropist Charles Hayden, was to give the public "a more lively and sincere appreciation of the magnitude of the universe . . . and for the wonderful things which are daily occurring in the universe."

BOTTOM RIGHT The lower half of the sphere houses the Hayden Big Bang Theater. A dramatic visualization draws on the Digital Universe Atlas to take visitors from the island of Manhattan back to the radiant birth of the universe and forward through the formation of the stars and galaxies.

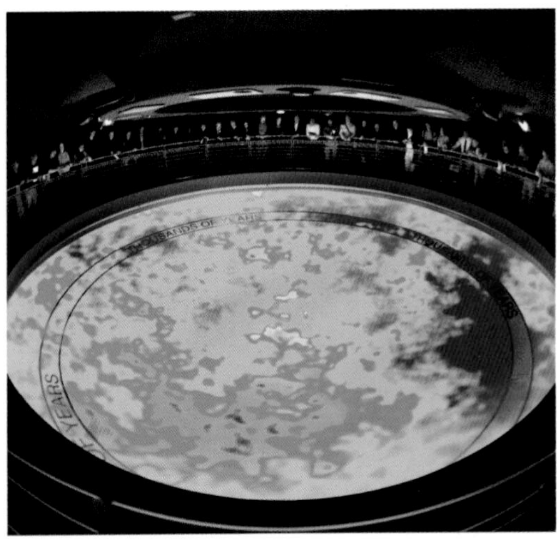

SPACE SHOW

Jaw-dropping and mind-boggling, the Space Show might *feel* like science fiction, but don't be fooled. It's an extremely precise visualization based on authentic data from the Digital Universe Atlas, a three-dimensional map of the known universe based on millions of ongoing astronomical observations and on physics-based simulations. Scientists are involved at every step of the 18-month production process for each show, collaborating with writers, artists, producers, experts, composers, and colleagues around the world to present the best, most current understanding of astrophysical phenomena, from the way collisions drive the evolution of the universe to the life and death of stars.

HARRIET AND
ROBERT HEILBRUNN

COSMIC PATHWAY

How long ago was the Big Bang? How did the cosmos and our own planet Earth take shape afterward?

Find out on the Heilbrunn Cosmic Pathway, a 360-foot (110-meter)-long timeline that spirals down from the Hayden Big Bang Theater and lays out the history of the universe. At the top, visitors can measure how many years a single footstep covers (on average 75 million), then traverse 13 billion years of cosmic evolution as they stroll down the ramp. Markers denote the passage of each billion years, the relative size of the universe at that time, and milestones such as the first generation of stars, the formation of our own Milky Way galaxy, and the evolution of life. Observations of cosmic objects whose light began the journey to Earth billions of years ago are followed by the oldest-known rocks and other terrestrial samples. Panels at the beginning of the pathway have been left blank in anticipation of the discovery of even older phenomena whose light has yet to be detected. At the end, the entire duration of human history is represented in the thickness of a human hair.

SCALES OF THE UNIVERSE

If the Hayden Sphere were the size of the Sun, how big would Earth be? (Grapefruit size.)

If the sphere represents the width of the Milky Way, how big is a typical star cluster within it? (As big as a baseball.) If the sphere were the size of a raindrop, how big would a red blood cell be? (The size of your hand.) Conveying this mind-boggling range of sizes was arguably the toughest challenge faced by the team of scientists, educators, and artists who collaborated on the Rose Center for Earth and Space. What ingenious tool did they use to meet it? Elements of the planetarium itself: the Scales of the Universe, a 400-foot (122-meter)-long walkway that hugs the glass curtain wall just below the equator of the giant sphere that serves as a basis for comparison throughout. Along the walkway, stations use the powers of ten to illustrate the relative size of objects that range from galaxies to subatomic particles. This firsthand encounter with scale across astronomy, biology, and atomic physics imparts a vivid sense of our place in space.

DOROTHY AND LEWIS B. CULLMAN

HALL OF THE UNIVERSE

This airy 7,000-square-foot (650-square-meter) space explores fundamental questions about the universe.

How did it begin? How did galaxies, stars, and planets form? How are the building blocks of life born within stars? Hall highlights include the Black Hole Theater, where visualizations convey the crush of gravity and the warping of time and space; a 3-foot (90-centimeter) disk of fluid that illustrates convection inside the Sun; projections of supernova explosions and of the seething surface of the Sun; exhibits that explore asteroid and comet impacts; and the AstroBulletin, which showcases up-to-date images and news from the cosmos on a 13.5-foot (4-meter)-long high-definition screen. Perennial favorites are scales that calculate your weight on the Sun, Moon, Saturn, Jupiter, and a neutron star. Upstairs in the Department of Astrophysics, researchers on the cosmic frontier use the Museum's share of the Southern African Large Telescope, other observatories, and Museum and national supercomputers to study planets, stars, and galactic evolution.

BOTTOM LEFT Believed to be a chunk from the iron core of an asteroid shattered in a collision with another asteroid millions of years ago, the 15-ton (13.6-metric-ton) Willamette meteorite is the largest ever found in the United States.

BOTTOM RIGHT The closed-glass ecosphere, or self-sustaining habitat, is in the part of the hall that explores conditions necessary for life. Inside the sphere, algae that capture energy from sunlight are eaten by shrimp. Waste from the shrimp then fertilizes the algae.

PLANETS
The Solar System
VIDEO

DAVID S. AND RUTH L. GOTTESMAN HALL OF

PLANET EARTH

No drab rocks in dusty cases here. Instead, huge slabs of stone welcome scrutiny and touch, and each has a tale to tell.

Continents drift, mountains erode, oceans form, glaciers flow, and the chemical building blocks of life cycle through crust and mantle to sustain our dynamic home. These 168 spectacular specimens were culled from 82 tons (74 metric tons) of rock and ore brought back by 28 expeditions from places as far away as Antarctica and as close as Central Park. The oldest, a zircon crystal from Australia, is more than 4 billion years old. The youngest, a chunk of sulfur, was collected the day it solidified in an Indonesian volcano in 1998. Towering sulfide chimneys show where life may have first emerged in the crushing darkness of the deep-sea floor, while an ice core from Greenland is a 108,000-year archive of climate change—one of the world's best preserved records. Like the ice core, the short documentary films about earthquakes, storms, or changing climate on the Earth Bulletin screen remind us that the story of Earth is still being written.

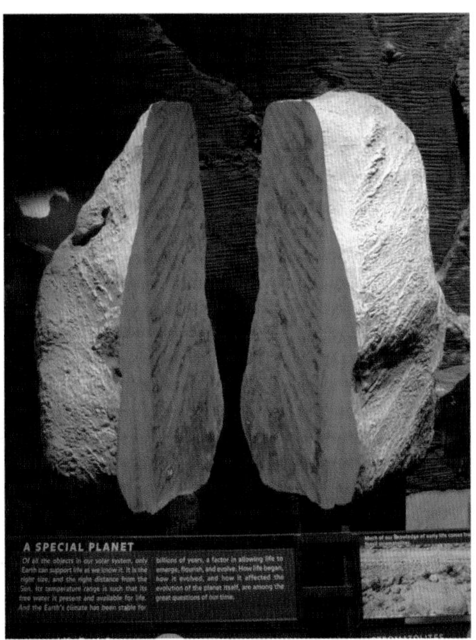

TOP LEFT Rocks can contain important clues about Earth's early atmosphere, which contained little or no oxygen. When photosynthetic bacteria in the ocean began producing oxygen, the oxygen reacted with iron in the seawater to produce banded iron formations like the one at far left. Specimens in this hall are terrific teaching resources for science educators, including those pursuing the Museum's Master of Arts in Teaching program.

TOP RIGHT AND BOTTOM Stromatolites are built by microbes, which were the only life on Earth until about a billion years ago and were the first organisms to photosynthesize. Scientists think that they produced an oxygen-bearing atmosphere and made it possible for life that consumes oxygen to emerge and evolve. The fossil stromatolite specimen featured in this hall was collected on an expedition to the Sahara Desert in Mauritania and is about 900 million years old.

ARTHUR ROSS HALL OF

METEORITES

Meteorites—fragments of planets and asteroids that survive a fiery passage through the atmosphere to land on Earth—are rare.

This hall contains more than 130 remarkable specimens, among them the oldest and most massive objects in the Museum. Leftovers from the formation of our solar system, most meteorites contain clues to how the Sun and the planets formed and evolved. Some tiny mineral grains found in meteorites even predate the formation of our Sun. In 1900 J. P. Morgan purchased the extraordinary 12,300-specimen mineral collection of Clarence S. Bement, a Philadelphia industrialist, and donated it to the Museum. Two railroad boxcars were required to transfer the collection, and the 580 meteorites it contained form the nucleus of this collection, one of the world's finest. Their scientific value has soared, along with advances in technology that help interpret the information these ancient samples of other worlds contain. New additions to the collection include meteorites from Mars and enigmatic nanodiamonds that are over 5 billion years old. Three types of Moon rocks collected by the *Apollo* astronauts are also on display.

BOTTOM LEFT The largest meteorite "in captivity," Ahnighito (opposite) is so heavy that it is supported by six pillars that go down to bedrock. It is just one part of the much larger Cape York meteorite, which landed in Greenland thousands of years ago. Arctic explorer R. E. Peary found it in 1894, with the help of an Inuit guide, and brought it to New York on his steamer *The Hope*.

BOTTOM RIGHT Museum scientists used an electron beam to excite atoms on the surfaces of meteorite samples to map mineral composition. Amounts of magnesium, calcium, aluminum, silicon, calcium, and iron are shown in the grid below.

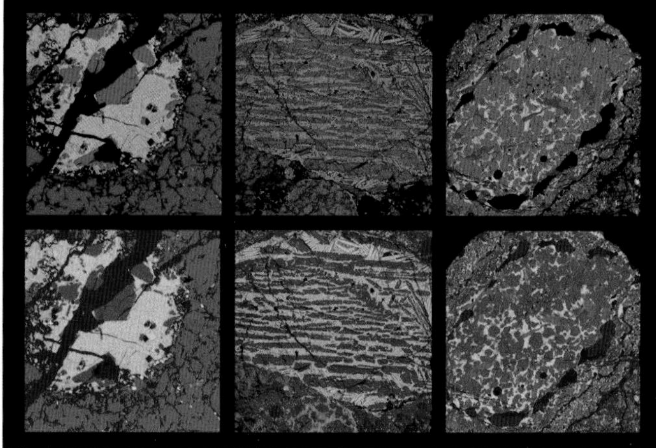

RTHUR ROSS
HALL OF METEORITES

HARRY FRANK GUGGENHEIM
HALL OF MINERALS
MORGAN MEMORIAL
GEM HALL

WHAT DOES A METEORITE LOOK LIKE?

HARRY FRANK GUGGENHEIM

HALL OF MINERALS

MORGAN MEMORIAL

HALL OF GEMS

Some 118,000 specimens—114,000 minerals and 4,000 gems—make the Museum's collection one of the world's greatest.

Less than 4 percent of the collection is showcased in these two halls. Almost everything in the Guggenheim Hall of Minerals came out of the Earth looking the way it does here, while the stones in the Morgan Memorial Hall of Gems have been shaped and polished to bring out qualities like sparkle, color, and texture. Treasures include the largest topaz ever found, a 4.5-ton (4.08-metric-ton) pillar of azurite-malachite ore from Arizona (opposite), a nephrite jade slab from Poland, and the 632-carat Patricia Emerald—one of the few large, gem-quality emeralds to be preserved uncut. Designed to simulate the interior of a cave, the halls also feature a re-created gem pocket (a crystal-filled cavity), synthetic diamonds, and specimens and models to teach mineralogy. The Museum's collection continues to expand thanks to an active research program in the Department of Earth and Planetary Sciences. Behind the scenes, geologists investigate why some volcanoes erupt explosively, the nature of jade, the consequences of climate change, and other planetary processes.

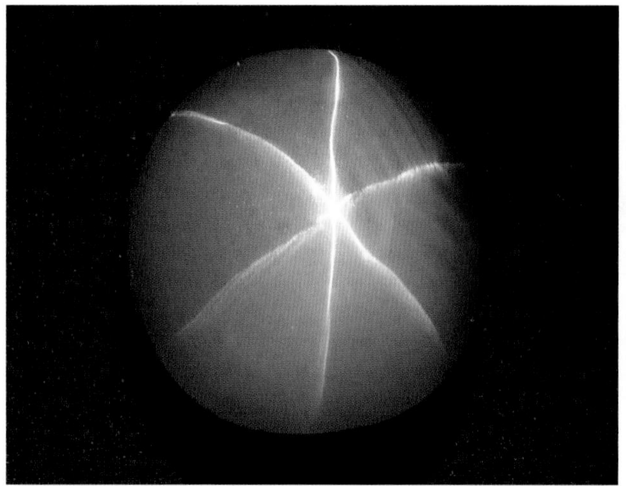

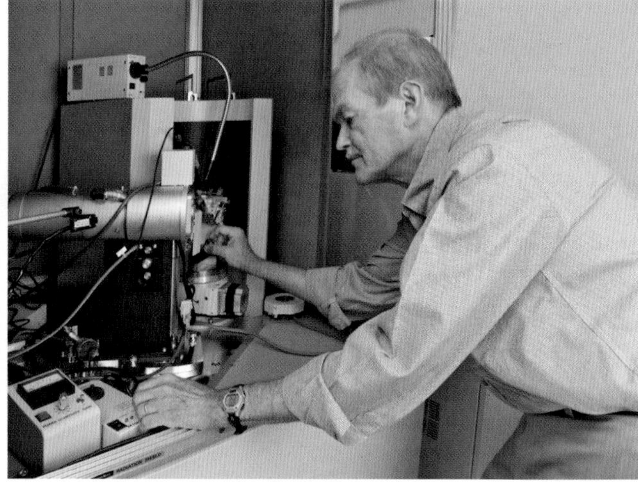

OPPOSITE LEFT Formed some two billion years ago in what is now Sri Lanka, the Star of India star sapphire is renowned for its size and perfection. The pattern, which appears on both sides of the stone, is caused by tiny fibers of the mineral rutile that reflect light.

OPPOSITE RIGHT Research facilities in the Department of Earth and Planetary Sciences include an Experimental Petrology Lab, a Fourier Transform Infrared Spectroscopy Lab, an X-ray Diffraction Lab, and the Microprobe Lab.

BELOW This legrandite crystal cluster, 9 inches (23 centimeters) long and from Durango, Mexico, is one of the finest specimens of this zinc arsenate mineral.

EXHIBITION AND EDUCATION

Visitors marvel at a re-creation of the ceiling of New Zealand's Waitomo Cave, where glowworms secrete threads studded with adhesive droplets that reflect light from their bioluminescent tails, in a recent exhibition.

EXHIBITIONS

Live butterflies. The Silk Road. Bioluminescence. Announced on colorful banners out front, these are the kinds of temporary exhibitions that the Museum produces every year.

They're an important complement to the permanent halls: in-depth explorations of wide-ranging science topics or an animal group. Mounting these special exhibitions is a far cry from dusting off some specimens. Each involves an intense collaboration between Museum scientists and an award-winning, in-house department of writers, artists, model-makers, architects, and graphic and interactive designers. Everything they create—from a replica of Robert F. Scott's Antarctic hut to an interactive display that mimics brain synapses in action—has to be beautiful, engaging, and scientifically accurate, as well as durable and universal (since at any time dozens of these shows are on view around the world in museums from Argentina to Australia). Part information, part narrative, part theater, special exhibitions are storytelling in three dimensions. All show scientists at work in order to convey that science is a career, a process, and a way of being and thinking in the world.

RIGHT Ever popular live-animal exhibitions enable the Museum to focus on a particular group of animals—lizards, for example, or frogs—and investigate their unique and shared characteristics. And, in a sea of taxidermy, what thrills more than the twitch of a tail?

BAGHDAD
VENICE
Europe

DISCOVERY ROOM

In the Museum's center for hands-on exploration, everyone is a scientist.

In the Discovery Room, kids' hands are all over the place: holding magnifying glasses, opening drawers of beetles, gingerly palming a Madagascar hissing cockroach, tugging on the jaws of a Kwakwa̱ka̱'wakw killer whale mask, assembling a fossil skeleton of *Prestosuchus*—a prehistoric reptile—or excavating a dinosaur nest. Young children come in for stories about stars or starfish, and then go looking for examples in the halls. On the upper level, older kids can track earthquakes in real time on a three-drum seismograph, or use a professional microscope to see what's squirming in Central Park pond water. Kids and their grown-ups can also meet scientists, ask questions, and observe specimens and artifacts that represent every field of Museum research. The conversation continues under the Great Canoe, throughout the Museum, or across the kitchen table. That's the whole point of the Discovery Room.

LEARNING FOR EVERY AGE AND STAGE

Thousands of students call the Museum home year-round. Preschoolers in the Science and Nature Program don hard hats on early-morning expeditions through the halls, learning to look at the world like naturalists. Adventures in Science summer camps introduce students through middle school to scientific disciplines and collections. The Science Research Mentoring Program gives high-school students the chance to work side by side with Museum scientists on yearlong science projects.

Teaching teachers has always been part of the Museum's mission. Today, the Museum draws more than 4,000 K–12 teachers for professional development every year through workshops, courses, educator evenings, and online offerings like the Seminars on Science courses. Urban Advantage, an innovative Museum-led partnership with the New York City Department of Education and eight science-rich cultural institutions, makes vast resources available to thousands of local teachers and students.

Finally, a range of programs make lifelong learning available to the general public, from the annual Margaret Mead Film Festival to monthly after-hours SciCafes, where cocktails and conversations about cutting-edge research mix.

STERLING
New York

An Imprint of Sterling Publishing
387 Park Avenue South
New York, NY 10016

STERLING and the distinctive Sterling logo are registered trademarks of Sterling Publishing Co., Inc.

ISBN 978-1-4027-9881-8

Interior design by MGMT. design

For information about custom editions, special sales, and premium and corporate purchases, please contact Sterling Special Sales at 800-805-5489 or specialsales@sterlingpublishing.com.

Manufactured in China

10 9 8 7 6 5 4 3 2 1

www.sterlingpublishing.com

Visit amnh.org for more information.

American Museum of Natural History Photography:
J. Beckett: 14 (top, with D. Finnin), 27, 89 (left, with A. Singer)

D. Brumbaugh: 48 (right)

M. Carlough: 64 (bottom right, catalog no. 80.0/784)

C. Chesek: 5, 26, 41, 46 (left), 56, 59 (top), 64 (top), 67 (catalog no. 70/10666), 68 (right; left, catalog no. 90.1/4854), 84 (with D. Finnin), 85 (bottom)

D. Ebel: 86 (right)

D. Finnin: 4 (bottom), 7, 14 (top, with J. Beckett), 16, 20, 21, 22, 24, 25, 28, 29, 30, 31, 33, 34, 35, 36, 38, 40 (right), 42 (right), 43, 46 (center, right), 47, 48 (left), 54, 58, 59 (bottom), 61 (left, catalog no. 16/8527; right), 62, 63, 66 (catalog no. 70.3/5650), 68 (top), 69, 70, 71 (center; catalog no. 30/7552), 72 (left, catalog no. 40.1/5176 A-D), 74, 77, 78 (right), 79, 80, 81, 82, 83, 84 (with C. Chesek), 85 (top right and left), 88 (right), 89 (right), 90, 92, 93

R. Mickens: 4 (top), 8-9, 10, 14 (bottom), 17 (top and bottom right), 18 (left), 19, 39 (bottom right), 40 (left), 42 (top), 44, 49, 51, 53, 55, 60, 65, 72 (top, catalog no. B/1618), 87, 88 (left), 94, 95

M. Shanley: 52 (top)

A. Singer: 89 (left, with J. Beckett)

J. Sparks: 52 (bottom)

E. Stanley: 42 (left)

K. Regan: 13

Courtesy Division of Anthropology: 71 (left, catalog no. 30/6332; right, catalog no. 65/1030), 72 (right, catalog no. 40/35.04); 73 J. B. Taylor (catalog no. 41.2/632)

Courtesy Department of Library Services: 15 (images no. 330591 and 330593), 17 (bottom left, image no. 318283), 29, 53 (image no. 333845), 64 (bottom left, image no. 2A21315), 78 (left, image no. 323194), 86 (left, image no. 2A3974)

Courtesy Jin Meng: 32 (top)

Additional Photography:
© J. Cancalosi/Nature Picture Library: 39 (bottom left)

© A. Mercierca/Science Source: 39 (top)

© T. Nadler/Frankfurt Zoological Society/AP Photo: 18 (right)

© D. Parer & E. Parer-Cook/Auscape/Minden Pictures: 32 (bottom)

© Field Museum/J. Weinstein (specimen of Museo Nacional de Historia Natural de Chile): 20 (top)

Endpapers:
Spessartine © American Museum of Natural History / Van Pelt Photographers; mammal ancestor illustration © Carl Buell. All other photos courtesy of the Division of Library Services and AMNH Photo Studio

1954

"Guide-a-phones" for visitors become available.

1955

The Museum establishes the Southwestern Research Station, a general laboratory for research into the natural sciences, in Arizona's Coronado National Forest. Today, it is a year-round field station for biologists, geologists, and anthropologists.

1957

The Department of Insects and Spiders acquires biologist and sex researcher Alfred Kinsey's gall wasp collection, the largest in the world with approximately 7,607,000 specimens.

1959

Selected to take part in a new program developed by the National Science Foundation (NSF) to train undergraduates in scientific research, the Museum takes on students to work directly with scientists in its laboratories and research stations.

1980

Museum researchers pioneer the use of cladistics, a method for analyzing relationships among organisms based on shared unique features that were not present in distant common ancestors.

1984–1985

Museum researchers take part in the Cerro de la Neblina Expedition to Venezuela's "Mountain of the Mist," one of several expeditions to South American sandstone table mountains known as tepuis, which yields extensive herpetological collections.

1989

The Mongolian Academy of Sciences invites the Museum to take part in a joint paleontological expedition to the Gobi. The following year's expedition is the first to include U.S. scientists since 1930.

1991

A five-story-high *Barosaurus* cast, the world's tallest freestanding dinosaur display, is installed in the Theodore Roosevelt Rotunda.

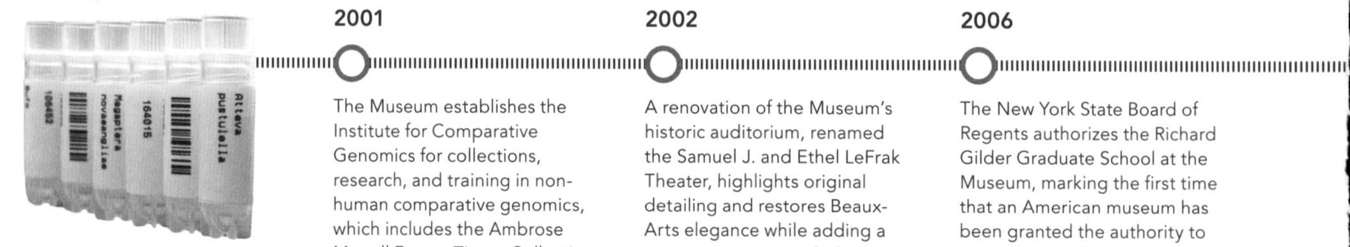

2001

The Museum establishes the Institute for Comparative Genomics for collections, research, and training in non-human comparative genomics, which includes the Ambrose Monell Frozen Tissue Collection, an ultracold repository of the world's biodiversity. In 2007, the institute is named the Sackler Institute for Comparative Genomics.

2002

A renovation of the Museum's historic auditorium, renamed the Samuel J. and Ethel LeFrak Theater, highlights original detailing and restores Beaux-Arts elegance while adding a new movie screen, plush seats, and advanced audio-visual capabilities.

2006

The New York State Board of Regents authorizes the Richard Gilder Graduate School at the Museum, marking the first time that an American museum has been granted the authority to award its own Ph.D. degree.